BUBBLES

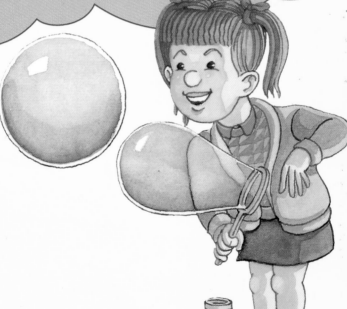

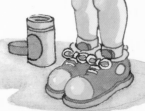

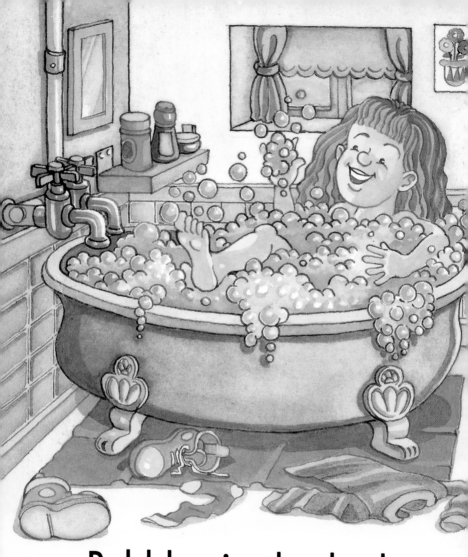

Bubbles in the bath.

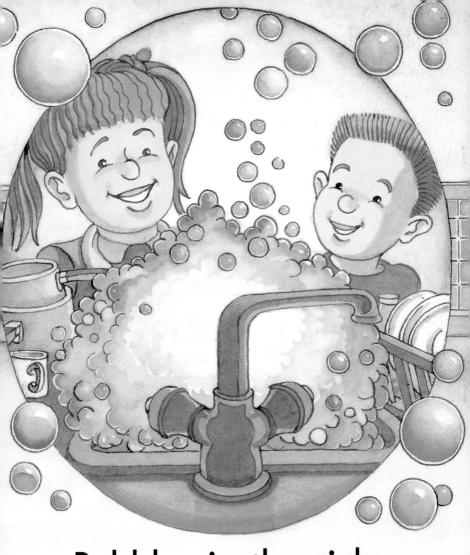

Bubbles in the sink.

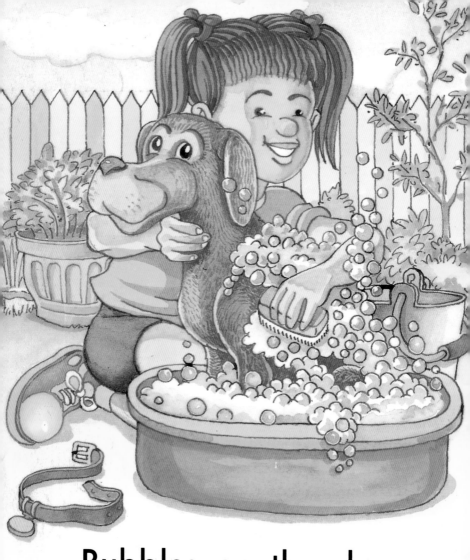

Bubbles on the dog.

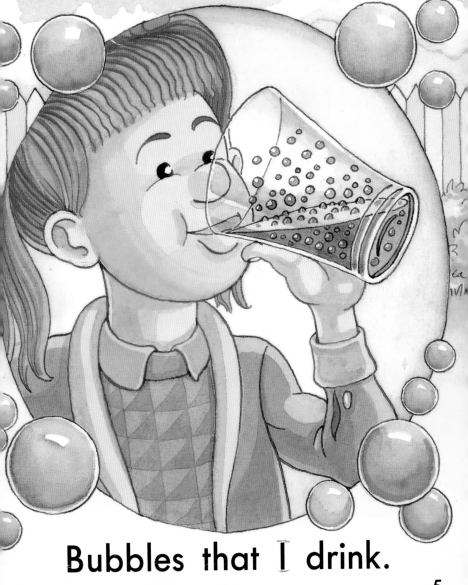

Bubbles that I drink.

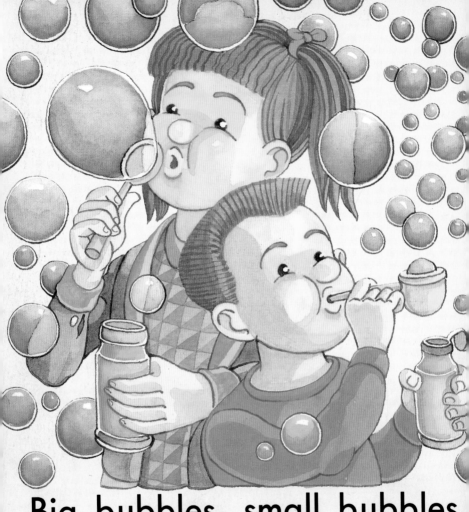

Big bubbles, small bubbles.

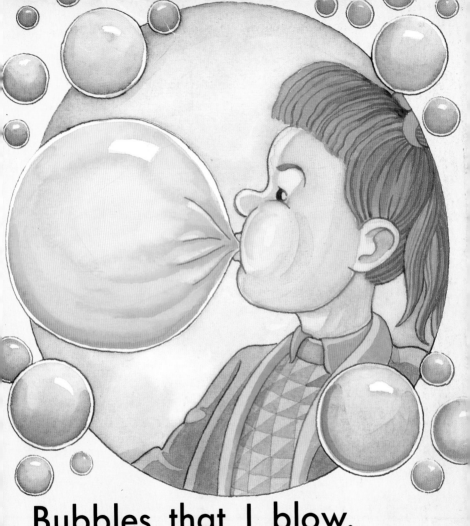

Bubbles that I blow.
Bigger, bigger, **bigger**...

7

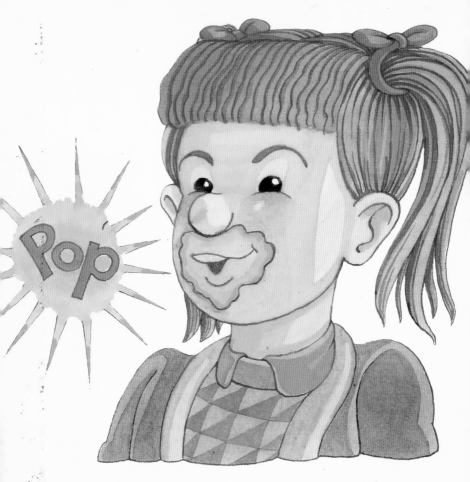

Pop! Where did
my bubble go?